CHAPTER 1

In the Dark

Kim was trapped.

"Help me," she shouted. "Please,
please help. Somebody help me."

There was no answer. The only noise
Kim could hear was SLAP ... SLAP ...
SLAP. Then again, SLAP ... SLAP ... SLAP.
The same noise over and over again.

It was the waves making the noise. The waves were slapping on to the boat above her head. Kim was trapped under the boat. There was no way out.

"Answer me. Please answer, somebody," she whispered. "It's so dark under here. It's wet. It's cold. Help me, or I think I'm going to die."

THIS IS WHAT HAPPENED TO KIM.

Kim had been out that evening in a boat. It was a motor boat and she was with her friends, Mark and Debbie.

It had been fun at the start. They kept close to the shore. But then they had gone out into the open sea.

5

It was getting dark. The wind was
blowing hard.

"It's fine," said Debbie. "No problem."

But then there was a problem. The
engine stopped. It just stopped dead.

"I'll start it up," said Mark. But he couldn't start the engine. Nor could Debbie. Nor could Kim.

It was raining. The wind blew harder and harder. The waves got bigger and bigger.

9

They put on their red life-jackets.

Debbie picked up the boat's radio, a

ship-to-shore radio.

"MAYDAY ..." she called. "Can you hear me? MAYDAY ... MAYDAY ... MAYDAY ..."

"What's that?" shouted Kim. "What's MAYDAY?"

"It's a call for help," said Mark. "They'll hear it on shore. They'll send the lifeboat to help us. We'll be OK, Kim. We'll be fine."

Just then, a huge wave hit the boat. It turned the boat right over, face down on the sea. It threw Mark and Debbie and Kim into the water.

It threw Mark and Debbie away from the boat. But it trapped Kim under it.

Kim was alone in the dark.

CHAPTER 2

The Lifeboat Comes

On shore, they picked up the MAYDAY call. Very quickly, the lifeboat came out.

"There they are," said the captain of the lifeboat, the Cox. "Two people in the sea."

"Stand by," he said to his crew. "Stand by. I'll come in close."

It was hard to pick the two people out of the water but the crew did it. First Debbie. Then Mark.

"Thank you. Thank you," said Mark.

"But where's Kim?" said Debbie.

"Kim was in the boat with us." She started to cry.

"We'll find her," said the Cox.

The lifeboat's lights were very bright. No one could see Kim in the water.

"There's only one answer," said the Cox. "She must be under that boat. Trapped under there. We need somebody to go and look."

"I'll go," said Steve.

Steve was the youngest man in the lifeboat crew. He was very fit and he knew how to dive.

But now huge waves were slapping the up-turned motor boat. The wind was getting worse and worse.

Steve took a torch, an underwater torch. Then he had to drop into the cold, dark water. He dived. He came up in the space under the boat.

SLAP ... SLAP ... SLAP went the sea. SLAP ... SLAP ... SLAP.

Then he heard a whisper.

"I'm over here," it said. "Help me."

CHAPTER 3

Only One Way

Steve saw a girl in a red life-jacket.

She was on her back in the water. Her face was very close to the boat over her head.

"Kim?" said Steve.

"Thank God," said Kim. "Thank God I'm not alone."

"We'll soon have you out of here," said Steve.

But he could see there was very little air under there. The air would soon be gone.

"Can you move the boat?" asked Kim. "Can you move it off me?"

"It's too heavy to move," said Steve. "Much too heavy. There's only one way to get you out."

"What?" asked Kim.

"Dive down and come up on the other side," said Steve.

"I can't," said Kim. "I don't know how to dive. I'd go down and never come up."

Steve took her hand. It was very cold. "I'll help you," he said. "Take a deep breath."

Kim tried to take a breath, but she was shaking. Shaking with cold and fear.

"I can't," she said. "I can't dive." She was crying now.

"Kim," said Steve. "Come on." He tried to push her down in the water. "Just a small dive down and you'll be free. Free in the open air."

By now, Steve had little breath left. The air had nearly all gone. And he saw that the boat was going down in the water. It would sink in two or three minutes. Then they would both die.

"Try," he said. "Please try."

"Leave me," said Kim. "Just leave me to die."

"I won't leave you," said Steve. He was fighting for breath now. "You can do this dive. Think of your friends. Think of your family at home. Please try now."

Kim said nothing for a minute.

OK. I'll try.

They had to dive three times.

The first was not deep enough. Nor

was the second.

But on the third dive, they went down, down, under the side of the boat. And this time they came up on the other side.

Kim felt fresh air on her face. Fresh,
clean air. And she saw Mark and Debbie.
"You were brave, Kim," said Mark.

The Cox thought Steve was brave too. He thought Steve should have a medal. A few weeks later, Steve was invited to the city. When the chief of the lifeboat service gave him the silver medal, everyone clapped. And Kim clapped louder than anyone.